Winston the Worried Wh...

Alice Griffin is a writer who has also studied in the area of health and social care with a particular focus on working with children and young people. She is passionate about merging these interests to create entertaining stories for children with a deeper message. Alice lives on a narrowboat where she home educates her 8-year-old daughter and writes for various parenting magazines. **www.alicegriffin.co.uk**

Heidi Rivolta is an illustrator and also creator of the successful French learning course, Bonjour Tonton! These fun language lessons use puppets, songs and stories to teach young children French and Heidi has been illustrating the accompanying resources for the past five years. She lives in Devon with her husband and two children. **www.thelanguagetortoise.com**

Winston is a blue whale and blue whales are the
largest animals ever to have lived on earth.
They are even bigger than dinosaurs!

Winston's Mum and Dad tell him that a blue whale's tongue weighs the same as an elephant!

Everyone knows that Winston will grow up to be big and
strong so they imagine there couldn't possibly
be anything for him to ever worry about.

But deep down Winston doesn't feel lucky *or* strong.

In fact, he feels a little worried about lots of things.

Winston worries because his Mum and Dad tell him that one day he'll become a fast swimmer, but he just doesn't feel that he will ever be quick enough.

When they show him how to dive down into the depths of the water, Winston worries about what's lurking down there on the ocean floor.

But mostly he feels worried about making new friends because he thinks that everyone must be frightened of him.

One day Winston decides to talk to his Mum and Dad about how he feels inside and when they give him a big hug, he feels so much better. Then they listen as he tells them about each of his worries …

Winston tells them how worried he feels about diving down deeper and deeper into the ocean. How he finds it hard to hold his breath and has to close his eyes because he feels so scared.

Then he explains how he worries that he'll never be good enough at swimming because everyone in his pod is so much faster.

Winston's parents are sad he feels this way, but try to help him think differently about each worry. When diving they tell him to open his eyes and enjoy all the wonderful things that *are* happening, not think about the horrible things that *might* happen.

They tell Winston that he shouldn't compare himself to others, but instead always try his best and think about how much better *he* is getting at swimming.

But then Winston talks about his biggest worry of all, making friends. He feels afraid to talk to the other sea creatures because he is so much bigger and doesn't want to scare them.

Winston's Mum and Dad tell him he has the friendliest smile and kindest heart they have known and that he shouldn't be afraid because once he lets everyone else see, they will know it too!

Winston feels so much better after talking about his worries and realises that it's OK to be a little bit frightened but that when you talk about them, worries become a lot less scary.

He understands that the people who are important will always love him for who he is and that his Mum and Dad will only ever encourage him to do the best that *he* can.

The next day when Winston heads off to practise his diving,
he decides not to hide his friendly smile and
kind heart behind rocks and coral.

Instead, he waves and says hello to everyone he sees along the way and do you know what? *Everyone waves and says hello back!*

Further Discussion and Activity

When **small** worries are bottled up they can soon become **BIG** worries and for young children this can leave them feeling overwhelmed, scared and lonely.

Through the character of Winston we hope to encourage openness about any worries children have and with the suggestions below we hope you will feel able to initiate supportive discussions between you and the child(ren) you are reading to. **Enjoy!**

Before leading on to discussion and activity about their own worries, first encourage your listener(s) to talk about the story you have just read using the following questions and corresponding pointers.

Q. Winston's biggest worry is making friends, but do we think that all the sea creatures are *really* scared of him?

- No, they want to be his friend! We know this because in the story they say, "It would be great to play with him!" [page 7]
- They don't understand why he doesn't want to play with them!
- They think blue whales are really exciting and cool

Q. What about the little fish? He is near Winston a lot of the time!

- Perhaps Winston is so worried about *not* having friends that he doesn't realise how much someone *wants* to be his friend?

Q. Why does Winston think everyone is scared of him?

- Because he thinks he is different to them?
- Is it because he is much bigger?
- Perhaps because they are all together and he doesn't know how to become part of the group?

Q. When you look at all the sea creatures do you think they all look the same?

- Of course not! There are starfish, jellyfish, an octopus …
- So perhaps it is all in Winston's mind … OK, so he is bigger, but they are *all* different

Q. Let's think about how Winston feels …

- Shy about making friends
- Not good enough at doing the things his family are all good at
- Nervous to try new things

Q. Did Winston feel better when he talked about all of this? If so, how and why?

- Yes! He realised he was not alone in his worries
- It was reassuring to have someone tell him that he is good and kind
- He realised that it's important to have a support group where you can be yourself because then you can begin to feel brave

Activity
After discussion about Winston's worries and how he felt better, why not ask the child(ren) to share something they are worried about.

If you are part of a group you could ask any children who don't want to speak aloud to come over to you and tell you their worry quietly. You can then write it on an anonymous piece of paper and put it in a box. Once all the children who want to participate have a worry in the box, shuffle them around and read each one.

For each worry ask your listener(s):
- Why do you think you (this person) have this worry?
- How does it feel (would you feel) to have this worry?